Gary L. Williams, Esquire, is a resident of Laurens, South Carolina. He earned a Bachelor of Science degree from Newberry College in Newberry, South Carolina. In 1989, he was conferred a Juris Doctorate degree from the University of South Carolina School of Law in Columbia, South Carolina. He is the first person of colour to establish a private law practice in the City and County of Laurens since the founding of Laurens County in 1785.

This book is dedicated to all those voices searching for Freedom and Liberty.

Gary L. Williams

REVOLUTIONARY VOICES FROM THE SLAVE HOUSES

AUSTIN MACAULEY PUBLISHERS™

LONDON • CAMBRIDGE • NEW YORK • SHARJAH

A CIP catalogue record for this title is available from the British Library.

ISBN 9781398499904 (Paperback)
ISBN 9781398499911 (Hardback)
ISBN 9781398499935 (ePub e-book)
ISBN 9781398499928 (Audiobook)

www.austinmacauley.co.uk

First Published 2024
Austin Macauley Publishers Ltd®
1 Canada Square
Canary Wharf
London
E14 5AA

I acknowledge all who have been enslaved.

Preface

UNITED STATES' EMANCIPATION PROCLAMATION

"...All persons held as slaves within any state or designated part of a state, the people whereof shall then be in rebellion against the United States, shall be then, thenceforward, and forever free..."

– January, 1863

THE GETTYSBURG ADDRESS

"Four score and seven years ago, our fathers brought forth upon this continent a new nation, conceived in liberty and dedicated to the proposition that all men are created equal...that we here highly resolve that these dead shall not have died in vain; that this nation, under God, shall have a new birth of freedom..."

– November, 1863

THE UNITED STATES PLEDGE OF ALLEGIANCE

"I pledge allegiance to the flag of the United States of America, and to the republic for which it stands, one nation under god, indivisible, with liberty and justice for all."

– Approved Current Version, 1954

Up Above My Head

Up above my head,
I hear music in the air

Up above my head,
I hear music in the air

And I really do believe,
(yeah) I really do believe

There is a Heaven somewhere...

Song by Sister Rosetta Tharpe and Marie Knight, 1947.
Copyright of lyrics Princess Music Publishing Corp.

1

The beginning of revolution has always made people hesitate, for within the definition of hesitation, there becomes an unknown point of decision. The colonists had reached their revolutionary decision to begin a revolution and not continue being governed by a British Empire. This colonial decision was made, their muskets were loaded, and thereafter, there became "the first shot heard around the world". This revolutionary shot was made by the colonists at Lexington and Concord in April 1775, followed by Bunker Hill.

This revolutionary decision by the colonists generally became real in the colony of Massachusetts, and thereafter, throughout the other colonies, after Lexington and Concord and the Battle of Bunker Hill, when the revolutionary colonists began their point of no return. These battles fortified and changed the colonial landscape by continuing to empower the colonists' separation from Britain. From the very beginning of this revolutionary battle, if they would be victorious with their desire for freedom, these revolutionary colonists needed to be committed to the revolutionary cause, that is, committed to a complete change from British governance.

The revolutionary colonists did and won their freedom; however, their definition was a selfish ideation, since they never wanted freedom for all. With that first shot, the revolutionary colonists were clearly stating to King George III of England that freedom was what they sought, and freedom was what they shall have. They declared this revolutionary demand to King George III in their revolutionary declaration; their revolutionary clarion call swept down through the thirteen colonies, instilling a new spirit across this land's width and depth.

The spirit in the colonial air began in the mid-1700s, when revolutionary conversations of freedom from "taxation without representation" and revolutionary speech turned to revolutionary action. Loyalists to King George III fought to keep their wealthy lifestyle that they had created on these colonial shores. Both sides in the battles sought to keep their people, called "slaves", confined in the small, dark squares of the windowless slave houses, all occupying slave rows at this time and on the various plantations of the time; they sought to keep a free labour supply available as needed.

Interestingly, one of the men at Lexington and Concord who was shot and given his so-called freedom was Prince Estabrook, a "slave" of Benjamin Estabrook. Although he was freed, he was freed into a land where all were not free, and all people would not be free until 1865. Those who were not free provided the free labour supply to the revolutionary colonists, and Prince would also continue to supply the colonists with his valuable skills and carry his "false freedom papers", that is, a freedom handed out from guilt where Prince had to commit an extraordinary act to get a so-called basic transition to freedom. All our ancestors deserve to be recognised by all of us for their sacrifices, mistreatments, prayers, and tears.

Their lives centred on what these loyalists or colonists needed, desired, and demanded, and they need to be given appreciation and gratitude for their roads were rough and rugged. They prayed for freedom and longed for true freedom, and they instinctively knew that the colonists could not grasp the "revolutionary idea" of TRUE freedom for all, the kind that comes not from the mind but from one's heart and soul. The people living in the small, dark squares of the windowless slave houses also knew that if they kept praying, eventually they would receive freedom, and here at Lexington and Concord, onward to Bunker Hall and beyond, the first shot, that is, "the first shot heard around the world" for freedom and liberty, created a need by the colonists to have their minds firmly rooted in the type of freedom and liberty they sought, wanted, and desired, and the truth of the matter is that these revolutionary colonists, waving their red, white, and blue, wanted land based on a free labour supply. They wanted not true freedom for all but freedom for themselves and their progeny with a free labour supply that increased their wealth and happiness.

Their first shot announced their full intentions, even if it meant their death. However, the first shot of the colonists in 1775 eventually became, in 1865, the first step of the people of the small, dark squares of the windowless slave houses of this revolutionary land. Yes, the first step heard around the world was when the people of the small, dark squares of the windowless slave houses stood up and walked out of slavery into true freedom for all. They stood up and took the first step for freedom and the first step for liberty, all continued by taking the first step to finding a way out of no way.

They took the first step to finding their mother, father, sisters, brothers, aunts, uncles, nieces, nephews, cousins, and friends. They boldly stood up and took their first step, still praying for a clearer future. They took the first step towards citizenship, the first step towards due process, and the first step to state unequivocally, 'we the people'. They took the first step to letting that liberty bell ring for all. They took the first step of "not being judged by the colour of their skin but by the content of their character". They took the first step to the sacred words that then President Abraham Lincoln said in 1863 for a "new birth of freedom", and they took the first step to showing the world that they could help perfect this union.

For to perfect this union, true freedom came from the new citizens, that is, the former occupants of the small, dark squares of the windowless slave houses and from their hearts and souls for freedom for all. They took the first step heard around the world to reflect a marvellous idea, that is, if we all come together in the dawn of an all-encompassing true freedom, we then could become one nation, under God, indivisible, with liberty and justice for all.

2

Let the veil be lifted and true history shall be told that an American revolutionary battle occurred on 19 November 1775, the Battle of Ninety-Six. The revolutionary men, with their determination for freedom, such as Andrew Williamson, were committed to a revolutionary cause that was larger than themselves. They wanted a nation where everyone could have "life liberty and the pursuit of happiness", a happiness that would see that all their ancestral lines would become stronger, generation after generation. They wanted a nation where freedom would flow from "we the people", and to accomplish this revolutionary goal, King George III and his British loyalists were standing squarely in their carefully laid plans.

I can see in the revolutionary air of 1775, thousands of plantation owners and thousands of colonists coming to battlefields throughout the thirteen British colonies, demanding freedom. I can see men, women, sons, daughters, aunts, uncles, nieces, nephews, cousins, and their friends urging their fellow colonists on to victory. I can see on that revolutionary landscape some men, with the finest clothing that free labour can produce, coming down the hills and valleys of this land to lead men to victory.

They knew that their wills were strong, their philosophy was sound, their documents were well-written, and their determination was announced. I can also see and hear at the dawn of this revolutionary time the "people" of the small, dark squares of the windowless slave houses dotted across this colonial landscape. What of those people who were also confined by a selfish and greed-based ideology that the colonists and the loyalists sought their endless supply of free labour?

When one of the "slaves" was worked to death, the colonists would just casually go down to the slave auction blocks located at most colonial courthouses and buy another "person" or group of "people". I see and hear in that revolutionary air, these people seeking freedom and liberty for all. And on that Hard Labor Plantation of Andrew Williamson, I see and hear the "slaves" coming from the fields, coming from Williamson's "Big House" and children in the hot summer air of 1775 around Williamson's dinner table and southern wrap-around porch.

I can hear revolutionary voices in history's mist, shouting, "What 'bout me? What 'bout me, the one who has picked your cotton? What 'bout me, Massa Andrew, the one who has chopped your wood? What 'bout me, the one who is the free labour of your Hard Labor Plantation?" I can hear revolutionary voices in history's mist shouting, "What 'bout me, the one who cooked your meals? What 'bout me, the one who cleaned your house? What 'bout me, the one who made and repaired your shoes and made your clothing so that you could go on that battlefield of revolution? What 'bout me, who you used to increase your wealth through my womb placed in my biological frame by God?"

I hear revolutionary voices in history's mist shouting, "What 'bout me who look like you and your family, for you have placed your gene pool inside of me to carry down through the generations of time? What 'bout me, who you sought to be your bed-warmer and concubine?" I can hear revolutionary voices in history's air shouting, What 'bout my family who you threaten with beatings, separation, and sometimes death? What 'bout my mother, who you worked for your household, nursing and caring for your children until we buried her on the hill in the land of revolution? What 'bout my father, who worked in your fields of cotton day after day, coming into your small, dark squares of the windowless slave houses, falling on your old wooden floor, tired of working from "sun up to sun down", day after day and night after night until he was carried up the hill and buried in the land of this revolution? What 'bout my brother working your horses that you ride on that revolutionary battlefield and shoes your horse on your Hard Labor Plantation? Shoes so many horses through blacksmithing over the hot anvils of your plantation until he died and was carried up to be buried in the land of your revolution. What 'bout my sister, whom you impregnated and continued to breed year after year to increase your wealth until she was carried up that Hard Labor Road where the dirt covered her gravestone of time. What 'bout my son, who cut your wood year after year and then was carried up the graveyard hill to be seen no more? What 'bout my children, who were sold away never to be seen no more? What 'bout our confinement in your Hard Labor Plantation? Do we not count in the revolutionary history of time where we also revolt, cry, shout, and pray for our freedom and liberty, just like you?

These revolutionary voices in history's mist speak, yet today, shout, we were and are people also. We were and are children of a king that is universal. We started praying for the saviour to come in the revolutionary air of the 1700s and 1800s. We kept praying and waiting. The freedom Williamson desired was a selfish freedom. He wanted it all for himself and his revolutionary men. He never wanted his free labour supply to ever know the victory of revolution, but in their small, dark squares of the windowless slave houses, they kept praying as they kept coming and going to the fields, picking his cotton. They kept rising early in the morning to nurse his children, and they kept praying.

They would hear, now and then, names such as Stono, such as Vesey, such as Turner and Douglas. That northern wave of winds came blowing in like a mighty tempest that could not be contained. Men like Lincoln, Grant, Sherman, and others changed the calculation that was denied to the people in the small, dark squares of the windowless slave houses. They came stepping out with "life, liberty, and the pursuit of happiness", just like those revolutionary men of 1775, and thereafter, they lived the freedom of the men and women who kept them shackled down and who had only theoretically applied their declaratory documents for freedom and liberty. For the fact of the matter is that those revolutionary colonists in the American Revolution and the "Founding Fathers" of this American nation failed to realise that their most important battle was the battle in their minds, that is, the truth is that no man, no person, no people is truly free until we are all free. Free to speak our minds, free to live in the security of our families, free to see all our ancestral lines grow and move this American nation forward to a more perfect union, where we are one nation under God, indivisible, with liberty and justice for all.

3

British loyalists, as well as the colonists enslaved, the veil will be lifted, and true history be told that on 22 December 1775, the Battle of Great Cane Brake, an American revolutionary battle, was fought in Greenville County, South Carolina. I took a "Sunday Drive" near where this battlefield had been, and as I gazed on the memorial sign placed by the daughters of the American Revolution, I cried. I cried tears for the other sons and daughters whose free labour of yesteryear formed the foundation of this American nation.

This colonial land and the same American land after the revolution was won have allowed men, women, and their families to further build economic investments on the back of free labour. I cried for those who longed freedom and prayed for freedom in the small, dark, windowless slave houses near this very canebrake that once was within the mighty and peaceful Cherokee Nation. History details that a large contingency of British loyalists was within this canebrake, which is described as an area of land where people called 'Indians' once put up a defensive fort against colonists' advances.

For once one is within the canebrake, all noises can be

heard. Here, in the canebrake of yesteryear, Patrick Cunningham of Laurens County, South Carolina, originally from England, and his loyalists' followers hid from the revolutionary colonists. Cunningham also sought continued freedom for himself and like-minded men and women across the colonial land. The colonists took up arms against King George III and his men.

Each side vowed to fight to their death, if need be, for freedom had costs, and these men on both sides of the battle were willing to pay those costs. As the loyalists rode across this revolutionary colonial land, they found themselves in a canebrake trying to free themselves from the tracking colonists who sought them out, for these colonists believed in their Declaration of Independence that stated at the beginning of its announcement that "when in the course of human events, it becomes necessary for one people to dissolve the political bands that have connected them with another". These colonists believed that the British Empire was seeking "taxation without their representation". These colonists' written document stated, "We seek freedom from all of these unjust obligations." And their declaration to disband from England had tremendous words.

Those majestic words came blowing across this landscape with swiftness that King George III heard, and thereafter, the king sent his best men to end the revolutionary rebellion. King George III, with all his powers and majesty, could not overcome their desire for freedom, for the men who sought to be free were committed to this freedom principle by stating and announcing in the Declaration of Independence "that all men are truly equal". As Cunningham heard the advances of these revolutionary men in the canebrake of Greenville County, he mounted his big horse, and took a man named Daniel Fanning with him, and went deeper into the Cherokee Nation.

With the cold Carolina wind of December flowing into their faces, Cunningham was still a man who was consumed with victory and sought to continue the glorious, rich life he had developed near Waterloo, South Carolina, on his Rosemont Plantation with his beautiful wife. I am sure he thought of old Rosemont, his ancestral plantation on the banks of the Reedy River, whose flowers and hospitality were well known through the pre-revolutionary era. The people living on the small, dark squares of the windowless slave houses of Rosemont and their progeny were named by Cunningham or his family, that is, Patty, Simon, Robert, Morris, Ella, Seleta, Becky, Harry, Harriet, Ephraime, Maria, Katy, Nanny, Carolina, Jess, George, Billy, Granby, Joe, Dick, Jerry, Frank, Sam, George, Austin, Daniel, Jackson, Madison, Talbot, Manmore, Simon, Adam, Clifford, Charles, August, Jacob, Lucius, Dave, Andy, Bunky, Jim, Drostus, Nicholas, Manuel, Jake, Edmund, Tom, Old Charles, Amos, Jefrey, Moses, Joe, Primus, Jesse, Jim, Ned, Patsy, Fanny, Phoebe, Elsey, Julia, Silvey, Sarah, Kitty, Old Rachel, Edney, Molly, Celia, Peggy, Anna, Martha, Viney, Jenny, Priscilla, Matilda, Ritty, Mirian, Laura, Molly, Charlotte, James, Eliza, Norah, Issac, Jake, Jim, Ben, Alfred, Adam, Bluford, Jerry, Snowden, Willie, Allen, Mack, Horace, Shelton, Turner, Wesley, Sterna, Herbert, Theodore, June, Stephen, Richard, Jim, Ben, Elliot, Buck, Jordan, Joshua, Walton,

Jeffrey, Pearis, Oliver, Perray, Simon, Allen, Washington, Samuel, Willia, Levi, Patty, Katy, Harriet, Tirey, Phoebe, Rhoda, Jane, Michala, Francis, Isadora, Eugenia, Rutha, Hannah, Judy, Catherine, Polly, Nancy, Roda, Pamela, Fanny, Angelina, Lucinda, Cornelia, Laura, Ellen, Flora, and Ellen.

"Slave owner" Patrick Cunningham never contemplated the larger battle in his mind; that battle was that he sought to continue his rich lifestyle in the environment of his freedom, but he never wanted nor sought that his "slaves" at his death in his small, dark squares of the windowless slave houses be free. No revolutionary freedom for them, win or lose. Cunningham never wanted the people he called "slaves" to be free to live life across this great land, just like Patrick Cunningham. Cunningham was willing to face death by the colonists' swords, and he was willing to fight the colonists to prevent his lifestyle from changing down through the generations of time. As Cunningham rode his big British horse deeper and deeper into the canebrake and into Cherokee territory during the Battle of the Great Cane Break, he was trying to end the revolutionary war to keep his freedom and to end the colonists' zeal for their freedom.

He and Fanning's revolutionary horses galloped away from the colonists, seeking freedom, and from revolutionary men willing to give their lives to come from under British control. This battle was one of the important battles of this revolution, for it showed the British Empire under King George III that the colonists had strong convictions for freedom and liberty. These colonists showed Patrick Cunningham that they also agreed with John Hancock's large, bold, and unmistakable signature on the Declaration of Independence, which told the British Empire that it shall be liberty or death. This sacred Declaration of Independence document showed Britain that freedom is what they desired and freedom is what they shall have.

This Battle of the Cane Brake showed the loyalist, Cunningham, and all those who were taken prisoners, including the loyalist, James Lindley of Laurens County, South Carolina, that their resolve was to make that declaration a reality for all the colonists. For if a group of men would go into the blindness of a canebrake, they sought to be free. These colonists boldly drew their swords and, with revolutionary commitment in their eyes, sought to show that liberty was what they sought and liberty was what they shall receive. They sought freedom to return to their comfortable lifestyle of using free labour to increase their wealth and freedom to use their laws to control a population of people to their will. This ideation was led by General George Washington until a true revolutionary desire came from the United States President, Abraham Lincoln, who said let "this American nation have a new birth of freedom for all" at Gettysburg, Pennsylvania, in 1863, which eventually led to the revolutionary reality of freedom for all in 1865.

Thereafter, an American freedom to speak, an American freedom to seek an American dream for their children and children's children, and for all who truly seek liberty and justice for all, an American freedom to dream and to keep their families together, an American freedom to keep the fruits of their labours and not to be sold away from each other, an American freedom not to stand with gentle feet on the slave auction blocks of this nation and look upon the crowds of colonists and others, hungry and willing to buy we the people for their free labour and increase in wealth. This economic propensity ended at the doorstep of men and women named Lincoln, Grant, Sherman, Truth, Tubman, and many other like-minded men and women. This tragic economic and political system ended when the dispossessed and disenfranchised prayed to a king larger than King George III and who heard the revolutionary voices speaking in yesterday's historical mist.

These revolutionary voices in history's mist are powerful reminders to America's conscious that the truth of the matter is what the 1776 framers of the Declaration of Independence and the 1787 framers of the United States Constitution never contemplated. That is, the greatest battle between 19 April 1775 and 3 September 1783 was in the colonists and former colonists' minds; that is, no one is truly free until we are all free, and then we can perfect this union, where there is for everyone one nation, under God, indivisible, with liberty and justice for all._____

4

As I drove over the country roads of Laurens County, South Carolina, I came upon an old fort. Here in the 1700s, a Cherokee blockhouse was used to protect the colonists when they had disagreements with the civil and peaceful Cherokee Nation living on the fort's border. A European name was given to this fort by people who came after the Native Americans, for the fort was apparently named for a colonist named James Lindley and surveyed by his father, Joseph. However, the veil Will be lifted, and true history shall be told that during the American Revolution, the Battle of Fort Lindley occurred here on 15 July 1776. Lindley's Fort, owned by James Lindley, a loyalist, was taken over by the revolutionary colonist, Jonathan Downs. Downs was a leader in this community. The history books detail that Downs heard the possibility of an attack by a combined force of Native Americans and loyalists, and upon hearing the news, Downs and his revolutionary men came riding on their big horses shouting freedom on that summer night of 1776. Downs helped the Fort win a decisive victory in the revolutionary dawn of American freedom.

Who was this man named Jonathan Downs? Was he a man who truly, in his heart and soul, intended to give freedom to all? Well, Downs rode that summer night to the other part of his plantation, whereupon Fort Lindley was located. On the other part of his land was his "Big House", with his kitchen apart from his house and apart from the small, dark squares of the windowless slave houses. Here were people named Primus, Will, Jim, Judi, Little Judi, Harry, Peter, Little Jim called Pompey, Fannie, and Malure yearning for freedom, willing to die seeking the same freedom that Downs and his revolutionary men had boldly ridden into the summer night of 1776.

I hear and see Downs as he turned his big horse down towards the Fort's road of yesteryear on that summer's night, with bold eyes of determination, commitment, and resolve for freedom. I also hear the revolutionary voices in history's mist when the people who stayed in the small, dark squares of the windowless slave houses shouted with one voice, "freedom and liberty for all!" Downs had another ideation in his mine: not freedom for all but freedom for them, and that was freedom to keep using the free labour supply they traded for on the slave blocks of Laurens County and the slave blocks of his friend, Henry Laurens, in Charleston, South Carolina.

If no one speaks for the people in the small, dark squares of the windowless slave houses, here am I, and I boldly announce to the world that until all are truly free, we will only have paper documents that have been written by people that truly did not believe what the documents stated, mere words that ring hollow in an alternative universe of shame, a shame that permeates this land where

28

people are used for their free labour only to be thrown into the graveyard of forgetfulness. I hear their revolutionary voices from history's mist calling each of us to action after the revolutionary victory partially began at Fort Lindley; the question remained: was this land named America truly to be free? Would a banner or flag of freedom fly in the night air when enemies would come against this American nation, such as in the War of 1812? For during this Battle of Lindley's Fort, I can also hear on the same summer moonlit night of 15 July 1776, on Downs Plantation, a cry for freedom and liberty from one of Downs' so-called "slaves", named Primus, on the opposite side of Lindley's Fort, Jonathan Downs' plantation land. Downs could and would not see the people shouting their revolutionary voices for freedom and liberty. Downs and his revolutionary men could not see the people in the small, dark squares of the windowless slave houses and old Primus, who was inherited from his father Joseph, shouting in the summer night of 1776, and all his "slaves", who provided Downs with a comfortable life of free labour. Downs, in his arrogance, would more likely state, how would these people have the audacity to want what I want? How would these people have the audacity to think like I do?

But hear me completely and clearly: when a person has been trampled and let down by the injustices of life, when people work from "can see to can't", seeing their mother, father, children, grandchildren, grandparents, aunts, uncles, nieces, nephews, and friends sold, beaten, and killed, they want deliverance from and by a king. These people named Primus, Will, Jim, Judi, Little Jude, Harry,

Peter, Little Jim called Pompey, Fannie, and Malure on the Jonathan Downs Plantation prayed, prayed to the king of kings who was more powerful than old King George III of England. Prayed for the same freedom and liberty that Downs and his revolutionary men wanted that night in 1776 in the woods of Laurens County.

From the small, dark squares of the windowless slave houses, freedom's wind came blowing from the northern skies in the course of those events, foreshadowing the true freedom that would come almost 100 years later at Appomattox, Virginia, when men of goodwill took up arms in this same land and rode into the night air shouting "freedom for all". Freedom and liberty in a civil war where shackles flung open and the people of the small, dark squares of the windowless slave houses rejoiced, saying, "I am free to think the only race is the human race." On their first step into freedom, Downs and his revolutionary men had selfish mindsets, only thinking of themselves; however, men and women like Turner, Grant, Sherman, Truth, Tubman, and others persevered and made them realise that no person in any nation is free until we are all free. Free to speak, free to marry who they will, free to dream big dreams, and free to climb any mountain in life. For at the time when the idea is truly committed by all, we shall have one nation, under God, indivisible, with liberty and justice for all.

5

The veil will be lifted, and true history will be told that on 20 March 1780, the Battle of Charleston, an American revolutionary battle, was fought in the city of Charleston. This battle was the first major confrontation in the southern region of the thirteen colonies. Major General Benjamin Lincoln could not overtake the dug-in British loyalists, and therefore this victory led British General Charles Cornwallis to casually walk the ballast-covered cobble streets of Charleston, South Carolina. The British had come across the old Ashley River and through the Benjamin Fuller Plantation, and as these British Redcoats were marching across the Benjamin Fuller Plantation, through the woods into the field, marching up to the stables and "Big House" of Benjamin Fuller, they were so intent on holding the line against the revolutionary colonists' ambitions that they did not see the people.

Yes, those English Redcoats were too busy seeing through their own self ideation that they failed to see or did realise, but they didn't see or help the people of the small, dark squares of the windowless slave houses of this colonial land. These British loyalists were bent on quelling the colonists' ambitions and not rescuing the people of the small, dark squares of the windowless slave houses. People who wanted freedom prayed for freedom, looking for a Redcoat who had compassion and who truly knew freedom to apply their grandiose idea and true freedom's spirit to them. When these British regulars came out of the woods on the Benjamin Fuller Plantation, the people living in the small, dark squares of the windowless slave houses may have possibly thought freedom had come; however, as the Redcoats came passing through by Fuller's slave row, marching, they kept marching and didn't look into the eyes of men, women, boys, and girls who had the same revolutionary yearnings as the revolutionary colonists they sought.

For if they somehow looked into their eyes, they would see a people tormented by free labour and lack of freedom. However, the Redcoat regiment would have seen the tears of the people in which their troubles were never meant to be over through this revolution. The "slaves' revolutionary idea" was for all to be free and to tell the other people that this land would never be their freedom until all were free. In history's mist, I hear the revolutionary voices affirming that gallant definition of freedom for all.

The British's eyes saw that this land would never have freedom for the people of the small, dark squares of the windowless slave houses because the colonists would never voluntarily release these people of free labour. They would not reflect any possibility of their belief in true freedom, for if they did when they passed through Fuller's Plantation, they would have demanded freedom for every person. They were too busy quelling the revolutionary freedom of their like-minded colonists. I can see and hear revolutionary voices in history's mist shouting out in the revolutionary dawn of Charleston, South Carolina, "freedom and liberty, YES, freedom and liberty for all". In the revolutionary air of 1780, I can hear and see on the Fuller Plantation people called "slaves", who could be lawyers, barristers, doctors, surgeons, businesspersons, entrepreneurs, writers, Nobel laureates, poets, scientists, valedictorians, and salutatorians of this future American nation and on the Benjamin Fuller Plantation.

I can see someone's grandma, someone's grandpa, coming out of the plantation owner's back door and all the backwoods plantation doors of the thirteen colonies as the British were marching, marching, and running across the land, heading towards Charleston and beyond with their military intent in their minds, with their pressed Redcoat uniforms running to dig into the sandy soil of Charleston's landscape. I can see dear Grandma as her tears come down. Tears of freedom, tears of liberty, and tears of joy. She had been praying for so long and believed that her prayers had been answered after toiling in the "Big House" of Fuller.

I can see her standing there with her arms outstretched and a loving smile, shouting, "I knew freedom would ring one day!" I can see her outstretched arms shouting, "Welcome, welcome, now I can find my mother, who was sold away by old man Fuller. I can find the son I birthed so long ago, only for that son to be sold on Henry Laurens' auction blocks. I can protect my daughter from the onslaught of these men who seek her beauty. Freedom, freedom, freedom has come!" As she stood there stretching her arms, the Redcoats kept marching, marching, and marching on by Grandma with their bayonets and redcoats.

As Grandma slowly dropped her arms, she saw where they too had passed by all the people of the small, dark squares of the windowless slave houses on Fuller's slave row.

What did she shout when they kept marching by and left her in the back doorway of Fuller's plantation door and all the plantation doors across this land? In her revolutionary voice, in history's mist, she shouts, "What about me? What about me—here confined, here controlled, here nursing their children? What about me here tilling his fields and picking his cotton? What about me coming in late to the small, dark squares of the windowless slave house?" Well, as she turned, and as they all turned, seeing the last Redcoat marching away, they all turned and said, "One day, one day soon, we shall all have freedom."

"For our king is not their king. I shall keep praying and praying and picking and nursing, and one day those who have ears, hear me, those who truly hear, let their story be complete." The fact of the matter was that these Redcoats and all the Redcoats sent to this land to fight and those who stayed in England were coming from a society of people who also benefited from the same slave trade, the same free labour supply. They came from a land of England that had the very same small, dark squares of the windowless slave houses dotted around their land, the same culture, and the same people who relied on our free labour supply. They were the ones also at the end point of the triangular trade, where on the first leg of that trade you find them in the woods and cities of Dear Africa stealing men, women, boys, and girls and shipping us over with our skilled labour, with the same hands that built the pyramids, the same hands that carried the gold of Mansa Musa, the same hands that built the empires in a land that they called Africa. They shipped us across the ocean to this revolutionary land of peaceful Native Americans that they poisoned, killed, and took down the "Trail of Tears" in the very land of tobacco and cotton, and we kept picking, kept picking, kept picking, kept picking, kept picking from "can see to can't see" from "sun up to sun down", and they continued hearing of our slave revolts.

Next, the enslaved women took that cotton and placed it in a spinning wheel and made those spinning wheels spin and spin, and spin, and spin, and spin, and spin, and spin from "can see into can't see" from "sun up to sun down", producing the cloths that were then put on the ships and sent to England and sold to make everyone wealthy, and they walked around aristocratically on our free labour.

Now you Redcoats have the audacity to pass by me, marching on the Benjamin Fuller Plantation. The same British people who also had their free labour supply to meet all their needs until 1833, and that is why the Redcoats passed Grandma and the slave row of Benjamin Fuller. That is why they did not come to free Grandma coming out of Fuller's back door; that is why they passed by slave row; that is why they didn't look twice at the people in the small, dark squares of the windowless slave houses.

As they came marching on the plantation, the people, whom Fuller called "slaves", thought they would be free. The skies became beautifully clear blue; blue birds were chirping in the air; freedom had come, but the Redcoats carried with them a "false freedom"; they only wanted to quell the revolutionary colonists and get back to the comfort of England and their wealthy lifestyle, and then these colonists would then return to their own free labour supply of "slaves".

The Redcoats kept marching, and as their eyes looked upon them marching and marching, they kept marching on to Charleston. Redcoats saw Grandma and Grandpa sitting out there on slave row and the plantation doors across this land, and Redcoats kept marching. They saw the children crying for freedom and asking for freedom for their mother and father, but they kept marching. They saw sisters, brothers, aunts, uncles, nieces, nephews, and their friends yearning for freedom, but they kept marching, kept marching to stop the revolutionary colonists from their idea of freedom, and they knew it was not freedom for all. They knew that these people were needed and enslaved for their free labour supply on both sides of this revolution. The people loyal to King George III and the revolutionary colonists both benefitted from the people in the small, dark squares of the windowless slave houses.

However, I hear in the revolutionary air of 1780 Grandma standing at the plantation door in history's mist, and the fact of the matter, you should too hear them clearly shouting at those Redcoats that "if they knew true freedom, the kind you tell your children and children's children about, they would have stopped and allowed everyone to have freedom at all plantations". At the Benjamin Fuller's Plantation, it would have only taken a few moments for the people in the small, dark squares of the windowless slave houses on Fuller's slave row to tell them that if the revolutionary colonists win, tell them "our king is the one that sits high and looks low". The people from the small, dark squares of the windowless slave house should have told the Redcoats that day on Fuller's Plantation while they were heading to the Battle of Charleston that "this revolutionary freedom shall be transformed into true freedom in 1865".

It would only have taken a few more moments for them to free all. Someone should have told these Redcoats that true freedom from the heart and soul shall always come from above, for true freedom and liberty flow down from their king's precious feet to "we the people". The Redcoats and the revolutionary colonists did not truly believe in the freedom that transforms one's heart and soul and thereafter allow us to become one nation, under God, indivisible, with liberty and justice for all.

6

In Laurens County, South Carolina, William "Bloody Bill" Cunningham's determined eyes reflected a man hell bent for revenge of his honour. To be publicly whipped at the hands of his fellow colonists and unable to obtain rank with their revolutionary force, Cunningham became a loyalist, and with his military base camp near Waterloo, South Carolina, and near his beloved ancestral home, Rosemont Plantation.

Raised in the area of the backcountry by his father and mother, he struck out at the colonists, which included coming to the very heart of the city of Laurens. Here he raided the home and post office of revolutionary colonist Robert Anderson, a colonist fighting for freedom from the British Empire. Cunningham had a city residence and knew Anderson before the war.

What we do know is that William "Bloody Bill" Cunningham was a loyalist soldier who seriously caused bloodshed and pain for the colonists. In Cunningham's foray into the city of Laurens, he killed colonists and proceeded on in his "bloody scout" mission to Hayes' Station, Walnut Creek Plantation in Spartanburg County, South Carolina and beyond. To travel to his base of operations at Cane Creek, he could come right up and attack by riding one of the main roads of the city of Laurens, which is now United States Highway 221. He did this horse ride because Anderson's house was on this main road, just off the Laurens public square. Freedom permeated the revolutionary air; freedom-seeking men ran to each battle, willing to die for the cause that was heard by colonists on the Old Wagon Road from Pennsylvania and up and down the main road where Anderson lived. Cunningham tried to stop the colonists from obtaining their freedom.

He was one of the leaders of the British forces, or loyalists, who wanted to enforce King George III's tax. The colonists rebelled, seeking freedom. Cunningham always supported primarily King George III in all his ways, for he and his family had done well with their Rosemont Plantation. From England, they came boldly across the Atlantic Ocean seeking wealth and fortune and had accomplished this lifestyle. Here, William "Bloody Bill" Cunningham did not seek the same freedom for their "slaves". For in the small, dark squares of the windowless slave houses of Rosemont, a quiet revolution has been prayed on to a king that sits high and looks low and was more powerful than Cunningham's English King George III. Cunningham was like the colonists with their selfish ideation of wanting to use their free labour supply to increase their wealth.

These people living in the small, dark squares of the windowless slave houses at Cunningham's ancestral home wanted a life free of forced labour, free of whippings, hot boxes, and violent threats, and free of endless rows of cotton plants.

Maybe the battle that should have been fought was the intellectual battle in the minds of Cunningham and his revolutionary men; the point is, no one was truly free until all were free. Take for example, some of the people of free labour at Rosemont Plantation, that is, the Coachman Simon; Sam, the gardener; Robert, the house servant; Becky, the maid; Harriet, the cook; Billy, the carpenter; Granby, the carpenter; Joe, the shoemaker; Jacob, the field hand; Maria, the washer; Jess, the blacksmith; and Dave, Jacob's son. All these people prayed for freedom and wanted freedom, but they were confined to a plantation with the colonists all around them fighting for their freedom.

The colonists wanted to maintain their lifestyle of magnolia trees, flowers mint julips, and big dance balls, where they considered themselves the class of the class, aristocrats. Cunningham's bloody path laid out was not for these people; the victory won by the revolutionary colonists was not for these people. The slave auction blocks and tobacco and cotton fields are where these colonists wanted the people of the small, dark squares of the windowless slave houses to stay, so that they and their children, great grandchildren, and their ancestors could prosper off the sweat and labour of Simon, Sam, Robert, Ella, Harriet, Maria, Katy, Jacob, Jerry, and Dave.

One day, people in the small, dark squares of the windowless slave houses became tired of being tired, tired of going to the cotton fields, and by ways of life to flee from patty rollers and bloodhounds. Tired of driving that

40

old Cunningham carriage, tired of cooking, house serving, and blacksmithing, and not able to tell their children and their children's children that they have a future of freedom. They were tired of seeing their people sold and their families separated. Tired of July 4th ringing hollow. So, they prayed and prayed for freedom and liberty to a king who sat on a throne higher than a king in any earthly palace while the slave revolts continued.

They kept watching and praying for true revolutionary change to sweep this land. In 1865, they received what they already knew in their hearts: "all men are created equal and endowed with life, liberty and the pursuit of happiness". In my imagination, I can see Jacob and his son, Dave, standing on the front stoop of the old, small, dark squares of the windowless slave house of Rosemont Plantation. Jacob with a gleam in his eye, years of pain and torment strapping across his face but always God on his mind; I looked at twenty-year-old Dave, a young boy who had become a man, and said we are also free. You, Dave, have a future, not of cotton rows but whatever the heights of your dreams, only if you can strive to dream as large a dream as you can think. we are going to help make a more perfect union. All the colonists were thinking only of themselves for freedom. We shall make this land called America one nation, under God, indivisible, with liberty and justice for all.

7

The other day, I stopped by and walked some of the land of Musgrove's Mill Battlefield and the former Edward Musgrove's Plantation at Cross Anchor in the country of Laurens, South Carolina. I had no idea that my emotions would overtake me with a sense of history, which led me to imagine what this Edward Musgrove Plantation would really have been like when you pull back the idea of southern magnolia trees and mint julips. I casually walked to a Musgrove's Mill signpost that read in essence that "it was on this site that Edward Musgrove built a typical plantation with a dwelling house and various other outbuildings".

I searched to find the true meaning of these words. As current history details, the Edward Musgrove Plantation's land on the south side of the Enoree River and Cedar Shoals Creek was overtaken by the British troops, and a revolutionary battle occurred on the north side of the Enoree River on 19 August 1780, whereby the rebellious colonists who yearned to be free of England's control sought their American freedom. I reflected on this 1780 Musgrove Plantation and wondered as to where Edward Musgrove's slave houses, or, should one say, Edward Musgrove's free labour houses, had been in 1780. The slave houses more than likely would have been located behind Edward Musgrove's

"Big House", and his "Big House" would have been filled with the nicest furniture of Edward Musgrove's rich life and with Musgrove's assertion of his neutrality to the war. The slave houses would have been of small, dark squares near the woods, with no windows, and only dirt floors and wood planks, where cold wind would whistle throughout the wintertime. Slave houses of people held against their will, controlled, and who were unable to structure their lives to find their individual definition of freedom like the colonists.

In my historical research, I found their names to be Tom, Phillis, Judy, Kezie, Charlotte and a child who was born sometime after the Battle of Musgrove's Mill by the name of Joe. If anyone truly were not free and needed their freedom, it were these six people who wanted freedom, who had the feelings of praying that their family would stay together, and who also had the feelings of wanting their children, grandchildren, great grandchildren, that is, their ancestors, to be free to live in a world where they could enjoy life, and for everyone, including their ancestors, to live their life in the pursuit of their own individual happiness.

As I looked, there were no signposts of where the dark squares of their slave houses were or where they had also yearned for their American freedom. There is no American memorial to their existence, nowhere at Musgrove's Mill. I stood on the very Edward Musgrove's ground, where, more likely than not, Tom, Phillis, Judy, Kezie, Charlotte, and Joe were made to do the free labour tasks throughout their lives, and all, excluding Joe, were more likely than not made to bury the dead of that Musgrove's Mill Battle and to pick up the soldiers' limbs severed from their bodies with the musket balls and metal swords, and also made to tend to and see the wounded and the near-dead. Tom, Phillis, Judy, Kezie, and Charlotte must have personally heard the revolutionary cannons and musket guns on 19 August 1780, on this Edward Musgrove Plantation.

The American Revolution, which included the Musgrove Mill Battle, was never intended for them and never intended for the child, Joe. Victory was never reasoned so as to end the slave ships from coming to the South Carolina coast and other coastlines of the newly formed American nation. The revolution did not and was never meant to end Henry Laurens' slave auction blocks in Charleston, South Carolina, which separated families while the enslaved people's mother's, father's, children's, aunt's, uncle's, brother's, sister's, niece's, uncle's, cousin's, and friend's gentle feet rested on his slave auction blocks and other such slave blocks across the nation.

History records that in 1794, after Edward Musgrove's death, Kezie stood and was sold on the slave auction block in Cambridge, South Carolina, present-day Ninety-Six, South Carolina, and there was no revolutionary freedom for Kezie. For Tom, Phillis, Judy, Charlotte, and Joe, well, they were inherited with all the other personal property, that is, with the cattle, furniture, tables, and clothing, by members of Musgrove's family or auctioned off at the estate sale with Edward Musgrove's personal property. No revolutionary freedom for them. As I left the Musgrove Mill Battle site and the old plantation land of Edward Musgrove, my tears, yes, my tears for those voiceless people to have some hope due to the victory at Musgrove's Mill; my tears for all the voiceless people who lived in the small dark square slave houses all their lives; my tears to give voiceless people some hope that they also could hear Philadelphia's Liberty Bell ring, loudly ring for their freedom so they also could have pursued their individual and family's happiness, free of control.

Philadelphia's Liberty Bell did not ring for Tom, Phillis, Judy, Kezie, Charlotte, and Joe due to economics, whose present progeny has now become systematic racism. My tears became my prayers, my prayers for someone with a revolutionary zeal to come forth so that all could be free, and my prayers became my resolve to live life wholeheartedly for the freedom of NOW and to enjoy life in pursuit of happiness. For we live in the freedom Tom, Phillis, Judy, Kezie, Charlotte, and Joe longed for and which was helped forged in 1863 by the 54th Massachusetts, a black regiment of soldiers led by General Robert Gould Shaw at the Battle of Fort Wagner near the harbour of Charleston, South Carolina, where 250 men also died for American freedom.

This American freedom was also helped to be forged by men and women by the names of Turner, Grant, Sherman, Tubman, Truth, and over a century later, by a King, for as the founding document so states, "We hold these truths to be self-evident that all men are created equal, endowed by the creator with certain inalienable rights as life, liberty, and the pursuit of happiness." I am sure Tom, Phillis, Judy, Kezie, Charlotte, and Joe also shed their tears and said their prayers in the small, dark squares and windowless slave houses of yesteryear and on the long, endless tobacco, cotton, indigo, and rice fields.

Their tears also became their prayers, and their prayers became their resolve for Tom, for Phillis, for Judy, for Kezie, for Charlotte, and for Joe to pursue the freedom that they wanted and had been denied them at Musgrove's Mill. I shall be the voice for Tom, Phillis, Judy, Kezie, Charlotte, Joe, and all those who lived in the dark squares after the celebration of July 4th rung hollow for them.

I shall be their voice to have their voice heard at Musgrove's Mill. I will be their voice to have Philadelphia's freedom's Liberty Bell ring and to now ring for us all. We should all ring the Liberty Bell at least one more time for Tom, Phillis, Judy, Kezie, Charlotte, and Joe, and for all of us who seek liberty and justice for all. Let us remember that somewhere in the hallowed revolutionary ground of South Carolina rest the mortal remains of Tom, Phillis, Judy, Kezie, Charlotte, and Joe.

This journey has taken nearly two hundred and fifty years to a more perfect union, and hereafter and down through the generations of time and down through the ongoing history of the United States of America and the world, we must be Tom, Phillis, Judy, Kezie, Charlotte, and Joe's American memorial to always seek a more perfect union and to always remember the historical truth as to who were in those so-called "outbuildings" that were indicated on today's Musgrove's Mill signpost; it was people longing for freedom; it was Tom, Phillis, Judy, Kezie, Charlotte, and Joe. We must be their American memorial to continue to strive for a more perfect union so that we may have one nation, under God, indivisible and with liberty and justice for all.

8

The veil must be lifted, and history be told that on December 1780, the Battle of Old Hammond's Store, an American revolutionary battle, occurred in Laurens County, South Carolina. We may never know the thousands of "slaves" who were sold from the porch of Leroy Hammond's Old Hammond's Store in the 1700s, but what we do know is that Colonel James Williams and his Mt Pleasant Plantation near present-day Mountville, South Carolina, came to own this land where the mighty Bush River flowed. In this rich land, cotton was planted to allow his free labour people of the small, dark squares of the windowless slave houses, whom he called his "slaves", to pick his cotton and increase his wealth so that he could enjoy with his family, and, more than likely, so that he could put the very clothes on his back.

History states that this Colonel Williams' plantation was in Laurens County near Milton, South Carolina, of old and up from Hayes' Mount and Joseph Hayes' confiscated Edgehill Plantation. On the colonial land of old Hammond's Store, loyalists to King George III of England had gathered, and the rebellious colonists who sought their freedom and yearned for the day they would be free of control from this British Empire battled and won. The old Hammond's Store's land became Williams', and in the distance was more of Colonel James Williams' plantation land and had more of the cotton that was picked by the people he confined in the small, dark square and windowless slave houses. They in the quietness of the day and night and in the small, dark squares of the windowless slave houses shouted for freedom. Williams' Plantation had been confiscated by Robert and Patrick Cunningham, and as their headquarters in this particular area, the Cunninghams and the loyalists had renamed the plantation Fort Williams.

Hearing of the Battle of Old Hammond's Store, Cunningham and his loyalists' followers had fled from Fort Williams and returned to Fort Ninety-Six in Abbeville County, present-day Greenwood County. British Commander Charles Cornwallis, on hearing the heartless surrender of Fort Williams, decided the south and the southern theatre of the revolutionary war must be held. As I studied this military manoeuvre, my mind wondered about the people who lived in the small, dark squares of the windowless slave houses and who picked Williams' cotton so he could increase his wealth. Yes, what happened to them during this revolutionary time? Well, what happened to them is that a plan occurred where Williams' people of colour, or as Williams would have called them, "slaves", were secretly transferred to his father's plantation in North Carolina so that his "property" would be secure.

Just like Edward Musgrove at the Battle of Musgrove's Mill, who had saved his "slaves" from British confiscation by expressing to the loyalists that he was neutral as to the revolution, Williams' decision to transfer the people to North Carolina was a similar move by Williams to secure his "property", just like gathering his valuable bulls and cows into the barn before an unbelievable storm. For if these revolutionary souls stayed on Williams' Mt Pleasant Plantation during the time of the loyalists' occupation, they would have been confiscated by the British, and Williams would have lost his "valuable property".

I have always been told that what is done in the dark comes to light. My historical research has found that on Williams' plantation were Will, Aggy, Milly, Lewis, Charles, Abby, Buck, Nan, Ellick, Peter, Tina, Fill, Easter, Maryann, Tom, Flora, Sarah, John, Rose, Filles, Patt, Moll, Nat, Cato, Frank, Dina, Lid, Judy, Mingo, Linder, Pegg, Little Mingo, and Sam.

They also wanted and prayed for freedom. There was no revolutionary freedom for them. When Colonel Williams' "property" was appraised and inventoried, these people appeared from history's mist, listed within the horses, cows, and furniture. But also, in that 1788 inventory of Colonel James Williams, revolutionary hero of the War for Independence, is something that strikes my sensitivities and informs me that Williams' revolutionary soul was not ready for freedom. For within the list of black people, the appraisers listed that Colonel James Williams had one large Bible. Hear me and hear me completely, down through the ages of time, a universal truth is that if Colonel James Williams would have truly read the ideas of that one large Bible, Williams would have known that there is a king higher than the old King George III of the British Empire. There is a king whose laws are greater than the laws of England. In history's mist, these people with revolutionary voices shout to a king higher than King George III was or would ever be.

The people of the small, dark, windowless slave houses that appear in the 1788 estate were appraised, and there was no revolutionary freedom for them. They shout down through the generations of time to my spirit, saying, "Just where is the liberty for all?" They shout down through generations, expressing their views as to "where is the freedom for all?" They shout into America's revolutionary air as to where is the "life, liberty, and pursuit of happiness". When Williams' Laurens County estate was closed in Laurens County Probate Court, these people who had been confined on this plantation and other like plantations shouted in one voice; that is, they shouted that prayer changes hearts and minds.

They prayed for freedom and longed for the day when they could tell their children and their children's children that they had become free. They who provided James Williams and his family with their free labour in his cotton fields and kitchen house, they who provided him with their skilled labour of blacksmithing and spinning wheels, they who provided Williams and his family with tremendous wealth had no revolutionary freedom. They were passed on to the next generation of Williams' family like pieces of furniture and property, only to become confined still in this free labour society of selfish orientation and further to become the "property" of Williams' family members. In history's mist, their revolutionary voices speak to all of us.

They state that there is no justice for one human being to own another. No justice for a family separated, never

50

seeing each other again. No justice for mothers, fathers, uncles, aunts, nieces, nephews, cousins, and friends to be bull-whipped and beaten with lashes that cut and sometimes kill. No justice that denies fundamental rights and due process that you say are worthy of you from even King George III, whom you rebelled against for freedom and of which you placed in your Declaration of Independence and United States Constitution. Well, justice shall always come full circle. For in 1865, justice would come to free these people from the small, dark windowless slave houses in Laurens County and in this American land. we all began attempting, through reconstruction, to perfect this union of American states. The union that was based initially on selfish ideations of those called "Founding Fathers", with names such as Washington, Jefferson, and Adams. Those men who had won freedom only for themselves and not the people who lived in the small, dark, windowless slave houses of the newly formed America, Will, Aggy, Milly, Lewis, Charles, Abby, Buck, Nan, Ellick, Peter, Tira, Fill, Easter, Maryann, Tom, Flora, Sarah, John, Rose, Filles, Patt, Moll, Nat, Cato, Frank, Dina, Lid, Judy, Mingo, Linder, Pegg, Little Mingo, Sam, and all ancestral lines of everyone who lived and stayed in the small, dark square and windowless slave houses of yesteryear had no freedom.

These were the people who had provided the free labour to make the colonists and the loyalists wealthy. The framers of the Declaration of Independence and the United States Constitution who met in Philadelphia's Independence Hall stated in their sacred words that "all men are created equal and have inalienable rights of life, liberty, and the pursuit of happiness". The revolutionary problem was that these men of intellectual and philosophical theory did not mean these sacred words in their hearts and souls. They never meant for people who have toiled the tobacco and cotton fields from the colonies named Massachusetts, Virginia, Pennsylvania, New York, South Carolina, North Carolina, and the rest of the thirteen colonies to live in the revolutionary victory.

If they truly believed in their words, if they truly believed in the idea of freedom for all, they would have made the right decision on the cobblestone streets and byways of Philadelphia. They would have made the right decision at Philadelphia's Independence Hall. If the nation's "Founding Fathers" truly believed at the very beginning that this land in which they would call America would be the land of liberty for all, all those souls who thirst for freedom and who truly seek and desire true freedom and justice for all would have also been included. If they truly believed in their hearts and souls that this land would be for all those who are tired, weak, and yearned for a taste of true freedom, which God intended that everyone would have from birth. The truth of the matter is when we all as one people, one heart, and one soul, when we all have one revolutionary spirit, we as one revolutionary voice of true freedom. Yes, we truly live out the meaning of these initial words written almost two hundred and fifty years ago in sacred documents of democracy and written with so--called democratic values; we shall all be truly free. We shall then be one nation, under God, indivisible, with liberty and justice for all.

9

Let the veil be lifted, and true history be told as to how many "free men of colour" fought on 17 January 1781, at the Battle of Cowpens. Here, the colonists were successful with the help of Brigadier General Daniel Morgan and William Washington. The British leader, Lieutenant Colonel Banastre Tarleton, was defeated, and the revolutionary colonists changed the trajectory of the southern campaign. This Cowpens' victory would be decisive in the sense that the victory would lead them on to Yorktown and the surrender of General Charles Cornwallis. Interestingly, William Washington helped Morgan at the Battle of Cowpens; Washington was saved by a black man who was with his trumpet strapped around his back, and thereafter, when Washington became surrounded by some of the loyalists, the man, who also sought freedom, took a pistol, shot, and saved Washington's life. Washington went on to savour the victory and lived to see Morgan on his deathbed in 1820.

This man's heroic feat of saving Washington's life was painted in 1845 by the brilliant painter William Tylee Ranney. If this incident were not important, oil would not have been applied to canvas. As Ranney drew, I could see the determination on the hero's face as he helped Washington fight the loyalists. I can see his resolve for freedom. Maybe, if Morgan, Washington, Tarleton, and the revolutionary colonists believed, truly believed, in their hearts and souls that freedom should be for all, then all the people of the colonies and all the people of the small, dark squares of the windowless slave houses would be free. I can see this black man's face thinking of grandmas, grandpas, mothers, fathers, aunts, uncles, brothers, sisters, nieces, nephews, and friends when he stood upon that battlefield to help save Washington's life.

I can hear his revolutionary voice in history's mist saying, "No more slave auctions, no more selling me, and no more long days and moonlit nights on the plantation." His revolutionary voice in history's mist would shout, "If I can shoot this shot, maybe Morgan, Washington, and the other colonists would come to know the true meaning of freedom, that is, unless all are free, no one is free." However, no congressional silver medal and no revolutionary freedom for this young man or his family is reported in history's mist. What is recorded is the fact that Washington received a United States Congressional silver medal for his contribution to the colonists' revolutionary victory.

Time after time, it is shown that the revolutionary cause espoused by the colonists was never intended for the people who lived in the small, dark squares of windowless slave houses. Is the saving of your life important enough for one's freedom? The revolutionary voices in history's mist would shout, "must we have to tend your fields with our free labour supply for you? Must we have to cook your meals and nurse your children? Must we have to come to the coasts of this land on slave ships from our African homeland to be abused by your indecent behaviours? Must we see our mothers separated from us, our fathers separated, and our sisters and brothers, nieces, nephews, cousins, and friends separated from us? When our African princes and tribal elders were torn from their people into a land that now cries for freedom but cries for a selfish freedom for themselves and not all of we the people?"

Well, we also cry for freedom. We cry that one day we shall have a true freedom, where all may be free to enjoy this land and the world of liberty. We cry that our children may have the freedom to decide their future with no fear of the slave catchers' chains and stud pens of your plantations; to see our ancestral lines free from enslavement; and to see the freedom Morgan and William Washington secured was not a victory for all but for them and the like-minded colonists.

Their prosperity evolved from the American Revolution did not extend to the people who were the free labour supply before, during, or after their revolutionary victory. This young man in saving Washington's life at The Battle of Cowpens would more likely state that silver medals may last for a lifetime; honours are fine, but what I seek is true freedom. What I seek is freedom for my family, freedom from the slave auction blocks, freedom from the hot boxes, and freedom to marry who I want and raise my children and my children's children in peace and security. I do not seek anything from Congress, just a freedom for all, to live in peace and love, and to one day look up at the United States' flag and in my inner self, truly, know that I did my duty when liberty called upon me to help Washington.

I was called in my soul to save the life of William Washington, and knowing that when I see that American flag, I want to say here, truly and sincerely, is one nation, under God, indivisible, with liberty and justice for all.

10

The veil will be lifted, and true history be told that in February of 1781, the Battle of O'Dell's Ford, an American revolutionary battle, occurred in Laurens County, South Carolina. During that time, a colonist, John O'Dell, had a ford that stretched out and allowed people to pass over the Enoree River in northern Laurens County, just upriver from Edward Musgrove, where the Battle of Musgrove's Mill had taken place.

Here at O'Dell's Ford, a section of shallow water at the Enoree River was created so that men, women, children, and wagons could safely navigate their way across. Loyalists attempted to capture Odell's Ford, a strategic position in the backcountry of South Carolina. O'Dell and his revolutionary men, yearning for the freedom espoused by Washington, Jefferson, and Franklin, were attacked at this ford. The loyalists were run out into the wooded landscape of other revolutionary battles. In history's mist, I can see the men as they yearned to be free of British control, risking their very lives for the freedom from King George III of England and declaring in the brilliant Declaration of Independence that "in the course of human events, it becomes necessary for men to throw off the political bands holding them together and have…life, liberty, and the pursuit of happiness". This freedom is what John O'Dell and his revolutionary men who encountered these loyalists that September day in 1781 sought—this "new birth of freedom" for themselves and their children and grandchildren.

However, this revolutionary shout to old King George III did not apply to the men, women, and children on John O'Dell Plantation's slave row on that very Enoree River or other like plantation houses dotted across Laurens County, the State of South Carolina, and beyond where the colonists' ideations were to make a new life for themselves and free of British control. However, the men, women, and children who lived in the small, dark squares of windowless slave houses prayed for freedom.

Somewhere, in history's mist, I can remember an old church revival song from my youth; I can hear in history's air, as these people heard the mighty Enoree River roar on moonlit nights of long ago, they would be thinking of a song such as that revival song that states, "Jordan River, I am sure I will cross." Just like that Jordan River on the other side of the world, where these people of the small, dark squares of windowless slave houses thought that one day, one day, they "gonna lay all my burdens down by the riverside" of life. These people dreamed a dream of freedom, a freedom that all who truly sought could share.

My historical research finds that there were people at John O'Dell's place that he "never" sought to share in a revolutionary victory. They provided free labour to increase his wealth, while others across the colonial land were in the same predicament. They all prayed that God, in his infinite wisdom, would allow them to ford the stream of life and have abundant "life, liberty, and also the pursuit of happiness". John O'Dell had on his plantation people he called "slaves". Aaron and Katy, O'Dell also called them his "property", and he battled against the British loyalists not to confiscate his "property".

However, John O'Dell's enslaved revolutionary voices speak down through the generations of time. These people would come in their small, dark squares of windowless slave houses in 1781, tired and weary from O'Dell's cotton and tobacco fields, into that darkness of time. Quite frankly, they could be considered part of everyone's ancestral lines of anyone's ancestors that provided free labour to the plantation slavery system before 1865, from Edward Musgrove, Joseph Hayes, Joseph Kellet, Patrick Cunningham, William Cunningham, Robert Cunningham, James Lindley, Jonathan Downs, and thousands of other like-minded men.

These people on John O'Dell Plantation's slave row were hungry, tired, and weak, but they kept moving, yet moving, yet moving, yet moving forward into their unknown time of revolutionary change. Moving forward and striving that one day their ancestors would also reap the sacrifices of their time that they made on the John O'Dell Plantation and all plantations across this American nation.

In that darkness of those O'Dell's slave houses, I can see and hear Aaron coming in from the cotton field of time having picked John O'Dell's cotton from "sun up to sun down" and at the slave door, the one with just one step and no porch, the one that is small, dark squares of windowless slave house and where the cold winter winds come in between the wooden planks and sometimes cause pneumonia, and as he approaches that slave house, he sees in the distance out of his weary eyes, Katy coming from O'Dell's back door having cooked John O'Dell and his family meals since morning and having worked on O'Dell's spinning wheels, spinning the cotton that is picked by Aaron. It was that moonlit night on slave house row when they met in front of this slave house, where their little kids, who also had their slave commands, as well.

In my imagination, I also walk with them into their small, dark squares of the windowless slave house of yesteryear. Here they struggle just to keep one foot in front of the next and lay down in the darkness of that night on O'Dell's Plantation. As night goes by, suddenly, I hear two words that shake the other slave houses awake. I hear Aaron's revolutionary voice in history's mist call out in the middle of that moonlit night, freedom and liberty in history's mist. These words, "freedom and liberty", are the words that resound across their slave house and the other slave houses on revolutionary colonist John O'Dell's Plantation. I hear Katy when she responds to him with the same two words "freedom and liberty", and as the two in that dark revolutionary night shout into the darkness, I feel their pain, their suffering, their tiredness, and their weakness. I hear their prayers not for themselves but for their children and their children's children to have freedom and liberty. I hear those words—the same words the colonists shouted when they met the loyalists at O'Dell's Ford—only to run into the nightmares of revolutionary war. I heard the same words when Jefferson wrote the

Declaration of Independence. I hear the same two words when Patrick Henry said, "Give me liberty or give me death." I hear the same two words from the "Founding Fathers" sitting around the constitutional table at Philadelphia's Independence Hall. I heard the same two words when Philadelphia's Liberty Bell rang, announcing victory had been won.

The difference is that these two words of freedom and liberty came from deep in the recess of Aaron's heart and soul. These two words of freedom and liberty came from the heart and soul of Katy, who is searching for the king in the darkness of her world. The king that is over King George III. The king that can walk across the river without using O'Dell's Ford in any way. They prayed to the king who says I am and always shall be.

It is coming from a soul truly wanting and yearning for freedom; it comes from a soul tired of picking O'Dell's cotton. It comes from a soul tired of picking the tobacco; it comes from a soul tired of just being tired; it calls from all the small, dark squares of the windowless slave houses of yesteryear, yes, freedom and liberty. For where is the justice that one man shall own another? Where is the justice that you can use people until they are carried out onto the graveyard of time, some in unmarked graves and some only with a field stone at their graves? Where is the justice that allows a man to go to the slave auctions to buy a replacement for someone he has worked to death and just throw that one in a grave or send him "down the river" away from his family? Where is the justice in increasing your wealth at the expense of a free labour supply without being conscious of the wrongness of your efforts?

John O'Dell sought freedom, wanted freedom but did not want the same for the men, women, and children of his plantation. This is the error in the universal justice of time: that when one seeks freedom and liberty, true freedom and liberty one must seek it for all. For I can still hear Aaron's revolutionary voice awakening this American nation, travelling into time and over the years of the hot sun days of history to give them also "freedom and liberty", a liberty that will ring throughout the history of these United States of America. Aaron's and Katy's liberty and freedom happened in 1865.

For in 1865, a "new birth of freedom" came as President Abraham Lincoln said that all would eventually be free. Everyone was free to live, free to seek their dream in the boldness of time, free to worship, and free to speak. Aaron and Katy in the darkness of O'Dell's plantation's night spoke for all the small, dark squares of the windowless slave houses across the land on which the colonists desired their freedom. They were saying in those two words a universal truth, that is, that Aaron and Katy's family was just as important as John O'Dell's family. Aaron and Katy's family and all the ancestral lines of enslaved people all over this American nation had the same dreams for their children as John O'Dell and his wife, that Katy shared the same love for Aaron as John shared for his wife.

When these truths could be finally realised by all, then we begin to have one nation, under God, indivisible, with liberty and justice for all.

11

The veil must be lifted, and true history be told that in the late summer of 1781, the Battle of Ridgeway's Fort took place in Laurens County, South Carolina. Here, a colonist named John Ridgeway, the son of Samuel Ridgeway, had on his land two Cherokee blockhouses that bordered the Reedy River and where the colonists used when there were disagreements with the peace-loving Native Americans of the mighty Cherokee Nation. Here, Ridgeway lived and was one of the commanders of the Little River Regiment Militia. Both battles in the summer of 1781 and the one in September of 1781 were won by the British.

Ridgeway could hear the waters of that Reedy River as the loyalists came over to Ridgeway's Fort to quell their aspirations. Ridgeway and his revolutionary men included the backcountry colonist, Ridgeway, and all his men who yearned to be free and were willing to die for that freedom for their children and their children's children. After the American Revolution, Ridgeway sought the benefits of that victory by petitioning for a federal pension. On his pension application, he told of his many battles and had the other former revolutionary men affirm these revolutionary facts. What he didn't say on that pension application is that he didn't seek freedom for all. He sought freedom for those who would continue after the revolutionary war to use the free labour that was inherited, traded, auctioned, and used for their benefit. These people in the small, dark squares of the windowless slave houses across Laurens County and beyond were never meant to savour the joy and merriment of being free from a British system that desired to tax and hold the colonists for their benefit.

The tragedy of it all is that the "Founding Fathers", the revolutionary colonists, and all those men that gather around the fine, luxurious table of Philadelphia and who loudly rung the Liberty Bell, never thought of the "revolutionary idea" that no one is truly free until we are all free. However, one man would come—the United States' president, Abraham Lincoln—to give this American nation a new outlook on its progress after its beginning of "freedom". I can hear revolutionary voices in history's mist of South Carolina and beyond telling all who would truly hear that "free labour is unjust; free labour is for those who seek to use and abuse human beings for their own aggrandisement; free labour is for those who have a selfish attitude of me first and there is no second; free labour is for those who are arrogant to think that they are more privileged than others; free labour is not seen until there is trouble in the land of magnolia trees and mint julips". As these free labour people picked the tobacco and cotton of yesteryear, when they drove their carriages, fed, and nursed their children, they were praying to a God who was higher than the biggest problem that you gave them.

They were praying to a God who holds everyone in the palms of his almighty hands. Change came to this

American land when all were freed and the revolutionary voices in history's mist petitioned their king; the king issued their decree of freedom through people who understood freedom and liberty for all.

There was no doubt that shackles would be released and all things old would become new, and that is when justice comes full circle. When their prayers and voices of freedom and liberty drifted and mixed into a revolutionary wind of change, the souls, hearts, and minds of Lincoln and like-minded persons were caught up in the decree of the king that said, "I am 'cause I am." The civil war came from the year 1861 to 1865, and within that American Civil War, the Gettysburg Address announced a different dimension with their emancipation and freedom.

The people who had been used for so long held their heads high, stood, and walked out of those small, dark squares of the windowless slave houses with freedom and liberty in their minds, hearts, and souls. They began to perfect this union. They produced dreams of progress while bending their backs over the tobacco, cotton, rice, and indigo fields and remembering Africa, the land that held their ancestors' past and present. They walked into freedom shouting, "Let all of us form one nation, under God, indivisible, with liberty and justice for all."

12

The veil must be lifted, and true history be told that nearly two hundred and fifty years ago, the American Revolution raged in the County of Laurens, South Carolina. For many years, I have read of the Hayes' Station Massacre, whereby, on 19 November 1781, some Laurens County men who were British colonists and who yearned to be free of England were attacked by British loyalists led by William "Bloody Bill" Cunningham of the Waterloo area of Laurens County. The Battle of Hayes' Station was about a year after the 1780 Battle of Musgrove's Mill and only two months after Joseph Kellett's Blockhouse Battle of September of 1781.

Last Sunday, I took a "Sunday Drive" down the old, long back roads of Laurens County, past old, wooded barns and old, weathered fenceposts of yesteryear, and with each couple of miles, it seemed like centuries of time passed. As I looked out over the old fields and pastures, I thought of the tobacco and cotton fields of long ago, mostly with the small, dark squares of slave houses where people longing for freedom lived. As I drove, I came upon a smaller road, and in driving its length, I came to a gate and found that a few yards farther was the site of the Hayes' Station

Massacre. As I left near Hayes' Station, I came upon the small Simmons Creek, and as I stood there in history's mist, I returned to my vehicle and drove a few yards down the road. As I turned my head and looked, there it was: the "Hayes' Mount" of old, named for Joseph Hayes, and, more likely than not, where the town of Mountville, South Carolina, took its name.

We may never know whether Colonel Hayes was a colonel due to "Sumter's Law" implemented in April of 1781 by regional Commander Thomas Sumter and formalised by the colony of South Carolina in February of 1782, whereby backcountry men who joined the revolutionary cause would be allowed the rank of colonel and given an adult "slave" and maybe a bonus of other "slaves".

However, what we do know is that Hayes and these men of the Little River Regiment Militia sought freedom from British control, a control exerted by a British empire that sought to tax "their labour", a British empire that sought to control their home and their economic gain from the triangular trade across the Atlantic Ocean. Hayes and his men were like Patrick Henry of Virginia, who said, "Give me liberty or give me death!" Hayes' freedom and liberty spirit did not, however, include the people he called "slaves" on his Edgehill Plantation, or at his Hayes' Stagecoach Station and Tavern, or at any other plantation where men, women, boys, and girls of the small, dark square houses also sought the same revolutionary freedom that Hayes and his men wanted.

My historical research indicates that on Hayes' Plantation were Julis, Prince, Doll, and their children, Little

Prince, Jack, and a Little girl born about 1784. Colonel Hayes and his men sought their personal freedom from the British Empire but did not see the same for the people providing the free labour. Their freedom would not come after the revolutionary victory at Yorktown, Virginia. I am sure that, more likely than not, Hayes had a lookout on top of "Hayes' Mount" across the Little River that fateful day in 1781 so that the person could run and tell them that the British were coming.

Just maybe it was Prince who ran from "Hayes' Mount", the very one that I looked upon on this fall Sunday of 2021. Prince had to run down that mount, across Simmons Creek, this tributary of the mighty Little River that I watched as it meandered by and down through the thick southern woods and over the old cotton fields to Hayes and his men, for at that time Prince was about 48 years of age. Just maybe Prince should be considered Laurens County's "enslaved Paul Revere" running to tell Hayes and his followers that the British were coming! Additionally, Doll or Julis could very well have been the cooks that day before Cunningham came, for a cook was the most trusted. We may never know, however, what is known is that after Hayes' tragic death by the sword of Cunningham, Prince, born about 1736; Doll, born about 1751; Little Prince, born about 1778; Jack, born about 1780; and a girl child, born about 1784, were not freed into the victory of the revolution.

At the appraisal of "Hayes' property" in January of 1786, the deceased Hayes owned Julis, Prince, Doll, Little Prince, and Jack. No revolutionary freedom for them. By July of 1786, Prince and Doll had added to their family a

Little girl child. No revolutionary freedom for her. In April of 1786, a petition to the court stated that Hayes' former wife, Alice, had sold seven "slaves", that is, black people, to Samuel Aiken, and Prince, Doll, Little Prince, and the Little girl had been given to her father in North Carolina.

They had no control, no revolutionary victory, no revolutionary freedom. The long-ago voices of Julis, Prince, Doll, Little Prince, Jack, and the Little girl shout from the old free labour tobacco and cotton fields of yesteryear and from the small, dark squares of the slave houses of Hayes' plantation. Julis, Prince, Doll, Little Prince, Jack, and the Little girl's historical voices speak to all of us now, nearly two hundred fifty years from the small, dark square windows of their former slave houses that would have appeared on Joseph Hayes' Plantation of 1781.

If only they could speak, they would say it was tragic, having surrendered, the killing of Hayes and Daniel Williams and all his men by Cunningham's "bloody scout" mission, but do not forget that they as people also lived, and they were also people longing for freedom. Prince was born around the time of the Stono Rebellion in South Carolina, and if by chance all of them had lived to 1865, they would have finally heard freedom. Correct the history, and we shall add a Laurens County memorial to preserve their memory, for Julis, Prince, Doll, Little Prince, Jack, and the Little girl, individually and as a family also longed to be free. Julis, Prince, Doll, Little Prince, Jack, and the Little girl prayed for freedom and died also longing for freedom.

Eventually, the revolutionary war's victory in 1783 would be amended by a 1861 Civil War, whereby the selfish ideation of the men at Philadelphia's 1787

Constitutional Convention would also have to be corrected because the most important battle from 19 April 1775 until 3 September 1783 was the battle in the colonists' minds to understand this important fact, that is, no people are truly free until all people are free, so as to create a more perfect union and gallantly strive for one nation, under God, indivisible and with liberty and justice for all.

13

The veil must be lifted, and history be told that on 3 and 4 September 1781, the Battle of Kellet's Blockhouse, an American revolutionary battle, was fought in Laurens County, South Carolina. I took a "Sunday Drive" to a historical marker located on a western Laurens County bridge, where South Carolina representatives and legislators decided that this Joseph Kellet's location in Laurens County was worthy of remembrance, honour, and the registry of American revolutionary sites.

As I looked upon their historical marker, I thought of Joseph Kellet leading his men into the old Cherokee blockhouse and yearning for freedom, willing to die for freedom, to be free from King George III of England and the British Empire, who sought to tax them and keep most of the enormous profits of the triangular slave trade based on a supply of free labour. My historical research has found that on Joseph Kellet's plantation was a lady whom Kellet enslaved, named Jenny, and with Jenny were her two precious children. Jenny and her two children also wanted freedom, wanted to experience what it would be like to be free of control, to be free from a system that sought to benefit from their free labour, but Jenny knew that to rebel against this cruel slavery system meant death.

Today, I hear in history's mist Jenny's voice as she speaks to all of us. She speaks to be heard down through the centuries of time. Jenny would most likely state that if a man called Patrick Henry of Virginia stated, "To give him liberty or give him death", and he made this "revolutionary call" so loud that old King George III of England on his glorious English throne could hear, you all should consider me and my free labour and confinement under your many desires.

Let us consider Jenny, the "female Patrick Henry of Laurens County", and she would state if she could that she, her two precious children, and all those enslaved like them also sought this "revolutionary idea" of freedom, so as to "give her liberty or give her death", and that is why Jenny continued year to year and day to day to look for freedom, to pray for freedom, to fight for the freedom, and the freedom she dearly sought would not only be for herself but for her two precious children and all that seek freedom, especially those within this cruel slavery system.

As I came upon this Laurens County Bridge Marker, I drove past the American land that once held plantations, tobacco, and cotton fields and the small, dark squares of the windowless slave houses, where, most likely, Jenny and her two children lived through the cold nights of enslavement. I thought of their free labour, for they were the ones whose cooking skills, other types of refined African skills, and precious hands of strength kept picking the tobacco and cotton in the Deep South and beyond.

72

Yes, they kept picking, kept picking, and just if they kept picking, kept picking, kept picking, yes, kept picking from "can see to can't see" down the long tobacco and cotton rows, Kellet, his men, and King George III prospered. Jenny instinctively knew that if she decided to run to freedom, the slavecatchers of Joseph Kellet and other like-minded men would use the Fugitive Slave Act to return them to the old plantation. They would be whipped, maimed, and scarred, and with blood sprouting from their backs, they would become weak, and salt would then be placed on their bloody wounds.

This entire savagery would be done in front in the other people of the small, dark squares of the windowless slave houses so that they could get the message that you, who are called "slaves" and who seek freedom, were not free. No revolutionary freedom for them; however, these colonists didn't know that when Jenny and her two precious children bent down over those tobacco and cotton plants of yesteryear, they were praying, praying to a king higher than King George III of England. They were praying for a "revolutionary idea" and "revolutionary change" for themselves. Praying for a change to a cruel slavery system that separated families and kept them from the revolutionary freedom that Kellet and his men also desired. Kellet and his revolutionary men freed themselves from King George and England's control, but as for Jenny and her two children, they had no revolutionary freedom. They continued with their free labour and continued in the hot sun of yesteryear in this new American nation, with that hot slavery-type sun beating upon their backs and beating down on the endless tobacco and cotton rows.

In history's mist, I hear Jenny and Jenny's children's revolutionary voices speaking to us all in the revolutionary air of September 1781, shouting to us all who will truly hear that "she also sought freedom; she sought freedom for her dear two children on Joseph Kellet's Plantation". Jenny would state that she laboured on Joseph Kellet's plantation to one day feel the winds of freedom blow across this land called America, which, quite frankly, was taken from the gentle and peaceful people of the Cherokee Nation. YES, Jenny shouts down through the many centuries of time, just like the famous Patrick Henry of Virginia, who prospered from the many labours of black people like Jenny and her two precious children. Jenny speaks to give Jenny and her two children "liberty or give them death".

Today, I proudly give liberty to Jenny and her two children and to all who lived in the darkest days and nights of the 1700s and 1800s. I give liberty that I live, for their many prayers have been answered. Liberty that I live, for their living was not in vain. Liberty that I live to be their voice to ones that had no voice. Liberty that I live because of the thousands whose gentle feet touched the cold slave blocks of yesteryear. Liberty for the endless rows of tobacco and cotton that they picked. Liberty for all those who had to watch their loved ones being beaten by the bullwhips of plantation owners across this land. Liberty that I live because of the thousands of days and nights Jenny and her two children and her and my ancestors spent in the small, dark squares of the windowless slave houses of yesteryear, suffering through the insects and the cold nights, praying and seeking freedom. I give her liberty for the thousands and thousands of prayers over those tobacco and cotton plants of yesteryear. I give her liberty for the many tears they cried over family members that were sold away by these colonists, never to be seen again. I give her and all ancestors liberty that I live because they lived in the small, dark squares of the windowless slave houses of their quiet revolution. Liberty to find Jenny and her two children in the fullness of time and freeing them from the shackles and nightmares of a cruel slavery system whose ideations raise its head yet today. I give her liberty that I live to tell of the men, women, and children who heard the old bloodhounds of yesteryear trailing through the woods behind them. Liberty for Jenny and her two children who lived through the nightmares of family separation and death. Liberty for those who ran from the plantations seeking freedom. Liberty for those who were caught seeking freedom, returned, beaten, and maimed. Liberty that I live to tell of the endless days and nights; that Jenny and others just like Jenny, tired, weak, and hungry in those days and nights when they would go or when they would come from those very tobacco and cotton fields into the small, dark squares of the windowless slave houses of yesteryear. But to all those who have ears and will truly listen, I give them liberty, for there is a God who sits high and looks low on a glorious throne, more powerful and more majestic than King George's English throne ever was or ever shall be.

Jenny and her two children and all the ancestors who also lived, lived yearning for freedom, praying that one day they would reap the benefits of their many tears, their many pains, and finally, yes, the strength of their resolve was brought majestically forth beginning in 1865. I lay their historical marker beside Joseph Kellet's historical marker, which I look upon today on this fall day in 2021. I tell their stories of their endless struggles, their endless tobacco and cotton fields of yesteryear, but hear me completely: I tell the glorious story of their victory. Victory, for God has allowed us to live and Jenny's ancestors to live away from that cruel life.

Now, we as a people must continue to perfect this union that was attempted by other strong men and women with names such as Douglas, King, Truth, Tubman, Parks, and others; local men and women whose names were Perrin, Johnson, McDaniel, Rice, and others who guided us on this course from the dark days of America's reconstruction. If only we could hear Jenny as she calls from the year 1781. For if we did, we shall correct the history and add another Laurens County Memorial for Jenny and her two children, for they also speak down through the centuries of time. Jenny shouts to those who will truly hear that "her family was just as important as Joseph Kellet and his family, who had to raise arms against King George III of England to gain their freedom from the British Empire".

But the fact of the matter is one important truth: hear them and hear them well. The truth of the matter is that Jenny and her two children were also the children of a mighty king, a more important king, a king that sits high and looks low, a king that was also over the life of old king George III of England; this king that Jenny and her two precious children served and who protected them from all injustice was the king, that is, the king who says I am that I am and always shall be.

This king is the creator of life for all, and Jenny and her two children's prayers are now being held by all of us who truly seek freedom for all. Free to dream, free to be the best one can be, free to be judged not by the "colour of one's skin but by the content of one's character", and free for this American nation to live up to its creed so that we all will have one nation, under God, indivisible, with liberty and justice for all.

14

The other day, I decided to take a "Sunday Drive" to the country of Laurens County, South Carolina, to see the old plantation house of Colonel James Williams. This man was one of the revolutionary leaders who sought freedom. Let the veil be lifted and true history be told that in 1781, the Battle of King's Mountain occurred in York County, South Carolina.

As I rode to Williams' Mt Pleasant Plantation land, I rode the old country roads of Milton, present-day Mountville, South Carolina, and I passed the land where the small, dark squares of the windowless slave houses had been. These houses and land held the free labour for Williams. I came upon William's house frozen in historical time, for it had stood there while almost two hundred and fifty years of time had passed it by.

As I walked up to the front, I was extremely aware that a black man in the colonial period and Jim Crow era, where control was everything, could not be bold enough to come waltzing up and knock on this big plantation's front door. As I stood there, I became instinctively aware that a balcony above my head once held the feet and the confederate spirit of Jefferson Davis. Davis, on his route of flight from Richmond, Virginia, came down this very road in front of this house, having spent the night at Lafayette Young's house. Davis spoke on that very balcony that I stood beneath. Davis more likely cried on that balcony for the nation he hoped to have formed on the back of continued free labour. What led Davis to stop here? What led him to stop by Colonel Williams' old plantation doorway and balcony before he spoke and waved his hand farewell to all assembled on its front lawn? What led him to tell these people who he had led to destruction from a lifestyle of free labour? What led him to think of Colonel Williams so much as to stop when the federal troops were on his heels and stop here on that spring day of 1865? Before he was "President Davis", he was a United States Senator, and he may have studied history books detailing how, in 1781, Williams had led the charge up King's Mountain, charging Patrick Ferguson and his loyalists in an attempt to win victory and secure freedom for the colonists and to help form this American nation.

He may have read in that history book that Williams was from this plantation near Mudlick Creek, just south of Milton of Old and Hayes' Station. He may have heard about the Williams' place in the parlour of Lafayette Young before he had retired for the night. We shall never know, but we know that he stopped at this colonial plantation house whose house was James Williams before he was killed on King's Mountain for freedom and who helped the southern campaign for that freedom.

I determined, more likely than not, that he stopped out of respect for Williams and his family to say a few words while on his way across the Saluda River and on to

Abbeville and Georgia. What we also know is that Williams met Ferguson at the Battle of King's Mountain, and both were killed there. Both men wanted freedom, with Ferguson wanting a continuation of his lifestyle of fine material and a good family life. Williams wanted freedom to live as he pleased, to not be taxed unjustly by King George III, but Williams never ever meant the people he held in his small, dark squares of the windowless slave houses to benefit.

I can hear, in history's mist, revolutionary voices. For example, two of his "slaves", Will and Aggy, would state, "The Battle of King's Mountain was tragic for Williams, who died fighting for his freedom, but he died seeking freedom as he defined freedom." Will's and Aggy's revolutionary voices shout down through history's mist, stating to us all that we knew that freedom bells would ring one day, and one day this way of life would pass away.

They, in their revolutionary voices in history's mist, would shout, "They kept picking, kept picking in Williams' cotton fields day and sometimes night when the moon was full." They would shout, "A hollow victory was won; they won for they benefitted from the sweat of our brow, our skilled labour, and our work in their fields. They benefitted from the large crocker sacks as we picked and pulled those sacks along the endless tobacco and cotton rows. They benefited from the cooks who fed and nursed their children. But when Williams died on that mountain named for a king, I was bending down over those cotton rows, praying". Others on other plantations across this land where the colonists wanted freedom would say that "when Williams died on King's Mountain, they were praying to a king in the rice and indigo fields of this land, praying for freedom. Will and AGGY could have been in North Carolina on Williams' father's plantation with the other "slaves" so as not to be confiscated because he held me as his "property", but wherever I was, I was praying. I may have been on his Mt Pleasant Plantation, and I was praying to my king.

Yorktown came with the surrender of the British Empire by General Charles Cornwallis to General George Washington. However, it was no revolutionary freedom for Will and AGGY and the more than fifty people called "slaves" on Williams' Mt Pleasant Plantation. They kept praying and waiting, moving forward to the day that would not have any bloodhounds tracking through Mt Pleasant's woods. They kept praying for the day that they would not see their mother, father, sisters, brothers, aunts, uncles, nieces, nephews, cousins, and friends sold away, never to see them again. Somewhere also in history's mist, Benjamin Franklin was asked a question in Philadelphia as to what they, as the "Founding Fathers", had created. Franklin said, "A Republic if you can keep it." Franklin was not quite right, for all were not invited to become a part of that alleged republic.

It would take to the year 1865 and with the thirteenth, fourteenth, and fifteenth amendments to the United States Constitution to guarantee the people in the small, dark squares of the windowless slave houses were included, finally to be included. At that point, we as an American nation began truly conceiving of one nation, under God, indivisible, with liberty and justice for all.

15

Let the veil be lifted, and true history told that when General George Washington triumphantly tried to shake the hand of British General Charles Cornwallis at Yorktown, Virginia, in 1783, all were not free due to the American Revolution. When Washington, as the first President of the United States of America, closed his weary eyelids, all were not free in the newly formed American nation.

In 1814, Francis Scott Key wrote this American nation an anthem entitled "The Star-Spangled Banner". In 1812, Key witnessed a renewed effort by Britain to bring revolutionary change to the victorious people in the War of 1812. One of the song lines Key speaks of was personally seeing the banner or American flag in the night air of Maryland as the bombs' red glare flew over Fort McHenry. His thoughts may have been whether the American flag still flew over the "Land of the Free". Key during that time must have lived in an alternative universe, for with the victory at Yorktown, the success did not allow all to be free.

He must not have seen the small, dark squares of the windowless slave houses located in the Maryland countryside and in the City of Annapolis due to the red glare he perceived. He questioned whether the American flag still flew, and if he wanted an answer to the question, he would only need to return to his Maryland home and find enslaved persons supplying him with their free labour. Britain had emancipated their people called "slaves" in 1833 but had returned in 1812 to the newly formed nation, where Cornwallis must have hastily held out his hand of surrender to Washington at Yorktown, for they had returned to the land, wanting to change defeat to victory. However, Key was speaking of the new American nation, which was seeking their way in the world as a viable nation, still confining people in small, dark, windowless slave houses of free labour.

Washington had died in 1799, having not freed his own personal "slaves" until his wife, Martha, died in 1802. He freed his personal servant, William Lee, only upon his death, into a land where all were not free. Mr Lee, more likely than not, had a wife and children and other relatives still under the American slavery system; emancipation was not what he sought in his revolutionary heart, for he enslaved over one hundred people who lived in his small, dark squares of the windowless slave houses.

As Washington tried to shake the hand of Cornwallis at Yorktown, Virginia, Britain and the King of England accepted defeat. Washington never intended for his "slaves" or any "slave" to live free in his newly formed land that he knew well. He may have privately told others the gradual end of slavery was wise; he never in his lifetime intended that his "slaves" enjoyed the same revolutionary freedom as him, free of his control and free of his directives. The freedom that he won through hard-fought battles, from his New York campaigns to Valley Forge in Pennsylvania's heartland, did not include freedom for the enslaved, the people of free labour.

In 1799, as Washington closed his weary eyelids, his farewell address did not include the clarion call for black emancipation and reparations. His powerful voice at the 1787 constitutional convention in Philadelphia's Independence Hall did not appeal to the consciousness of the "Founding Fathers" for their freedom. For if Washington would have used the powerful bully pulpits of his time that he had at his disposal, such as when he was the commander and general during the revolution in creating America, he could have reached the intellectual thought of freedom for all. If he would have had more compassion for the black lady and her genealogical base at the New York Tavern when she intervened and saved Washington's very life from poison, he could have met a higher standard by announcing freedom to all. Time after time, President Washington had opportunities to show the revolutionary colonists and the world that he could rise above the inconsistent arguments of privilege and race.

Yet Washington, in his words and actions, led all to believe that he wanted only freedom for the colonists, not freedom for all. Washington and the colonists fighting for their freedom missed the most important battle they had between 1775 and 1783; for the most important battle was in their intellectual and philosophical thought, for they failed to realise that only when all are free, all have freedom; then and only then, we shall create the most powerful nation known to all. When all share in the human rights espoused in their Declaration of Independence, when all share in a constitutional framework that begins with "we the people in order to form a perfect union".

If Washington truly believed those words, he would have freed the people he held at his plantation named Mt Vernon across the Potomac River. Washington should have said to the broader American people and the political and military class he represented that we must free all who are living on our surveyed land. We must free them, for they are also people; they are people who yearned in their hearts and souls for freedom, people who want their children to grow up in a world that will not "judge them by the colour of their skin but the content of their character".

Washington should have said that these people from the small, dark squares of the windowless slave houses have provided free labour for me and all of you all through our lives. They have saved us from ruin and death. They were on top of the various mounts of this country as we fought the British and served as lookouts and watchmen and women along the roads and byways of this revolutionary land, and some have fought in the battles by our side while I and all of us were fighting this British Empire to secure our American rights.

President Washington could have stated, how through his presidency and his life, they have been there helping him with the work of his life that allowed his concentration to be elsewhere, such as the gallantry of Mr William Lee. Washington should have said, "Let us now make this land the true land of the free and the home of the brave" in my lifetime. For once we free all, we can be a bright beacon for the world, leading the world in every corner to show, by example, freedom for all. Instead, Washington closed his eyelids, and William Lee finally knew somewhat about freedom. William Lee kept praying and longing for the freedom of others, still kept longing for liberty for all. He knew first-hand of the ways of the slave system, while the broader world and other nations, including Britain, emancipated the people of the small, dark squares of the windowless slave houses, providing a free labour supply. As the presidency of the United States changed from Washington, Adams, and Jefferson, they also intellectually failed to realise this, as evident by Jefferson's Hemings affair and continued enslavement as he came and went up and down the back stairs of his life and wrote a document that was good on parchment but not formulated into reality.

Why didn't Yorktown, Virginia, change the revolutionary air in America? Revolutionary change would not materialise until a President Abraham Lincoln and a civil war came and ended at Appomattox in 1865, when finally America received a "new birth of freedom" and continued into an American reconstruction that was disavowed by President Rutherford B. Hayes, removing the southern federal troops and allowing Jim Crow to arrogantly walk the streets of America. It took a Parks and a King for America to truly see its inner self and for an American civil rights movement to expose America's lack of true freedom for some of its citizens. We must continue to perfect this union, even if General and President George Washington could not understand due to self-ideation. We today see the necessity that until all are free in this land of victory of the American Revolution, no one is truly free; only after freedom and liberty are formed and shared for all can we then truly state in our hearts and souls that we are one nation, under God, indivisible, with liberty and justice for all.

Bibliography

LEXINGTON AND CONCORD
BUNKER HILL

* "No Taxation without Representation", Boston Tea Party, 16 December 1773.
* Prince Estabrook of Lexington, United States National Park Service
* "We the People...", Preamble to the United States Constitution, 1787.
* "I Have a Dream..." Speech, the Reverend Dr Martin Luther King, Jr, 28 August 1963.
* "Gettysburg Address", United States President Abraham Lincoln, 19 November 1863.
* "First Shot Heard Around the World", Concord Hymn, Ralph Waldo Emerson, 1835.
* The United States Pledge of Allegiance (4 USC Section 4)

THE BATTLE OF NINETY-SIX

* Watson, Margaret (1970) Greenwood County Sketches, The Attic Press, Inc.
* "We the People…" Preamble to the United States Constitution, 1787.
* "Life, Liberty and the Pursuit of Happiness…", United States Declaration of Independence, 1776.
* The United States Pledge of Allegiance (4 USC Section 4)

THE BATTLE OF GREAT CANE BRAKE

* Snipes, Christy (1992). Rosemont Plantation.
* Last Will and Testament/Inventory and Appraisement, the Estate of Robert Cunningham, Laurens County, S.C. Probate Court, Bundle (Box) 193, Package 12.
* The United States Pledge of Allegiance (4 USC Section 4)

THE BATTLE OF LINDLEY'S FORT

* Inventory and Appraisement, the Estate of James Lindley, Laurens County Probate Court, Estate Record Book, A-1, Pages 16–17, and Page 276
* Last Will and Testament/Inventory and Appraisement, the Estate of Joseph Downs,

Laurens County, S.C. Probate Court, Bundle (Box) 20, Package 7.

* Last Will and Testament/Inventory and Appraisement, the Estate of Jonathan Downs, Laurens County, S.C. Probate Court, Bundle (Box) 22 at Package 13.

* The United States Pledge of Allegiance (4 USC Section 4)

THE BATTLE OF CHARLESTON

* Benjamin Fuller's Plantation, South Carolina Historical Magazine

* The Slave Trade Act, 1807 (England).

* "We the People...", Preamble to the United States Constitution, 1787.

* The United States Pledge of Allegiance (4 USC Section 4)

WILLIAM "BLOODY BILL" CUNNINGHAM

* Last Will and Testament/Inventory and Appraisement, the Estate of Robert Cunningham, Laurens County, S.C. Probate Court, Bundle (Box) 193 at Page 12.

* Snipes Christy (1992). Rosemont Plantation.

* "All men are created equal...", United States Declaration of Independence, 1776.

* The United States Pledge of Allegiance (4 USC Section 4)

THE BATTLE OF MUSGROVE'S MILL

* Last Will and Testament/Inventory and Appraisement, the Estate of Edward Musgrove, Laurens, S.C. Probate Court Estate Record Book A-1, Pages 28–30.
* 54th Massachusetts, Colonel Robert Gould Shaw, 1863, US National Park Service
* "We hold these Truths…", United States Declaration of Independence, 1776.
* The United States Pledge of Allegiance (4 USC Section 4)

THE BATTLE OF HAMMOND'S STORE

* Inventory and Appraisement the Estate of James Williams, Laurens County, S C Probate Court, Estate Record Book A-1, Page 253
* "Life, Liberty and the Pursuit of Happiness…", United States Declaration of Independence, 1776
* Statue of Liberty, 1884, United States National Park Service
* The United States Pledge of Allegiance (4 USC Section 4)

THE BATTLE OF COWPENS

* William Tylee Ranney, South Carolina State House Collection, "Battle of Cowpens", 1845
* Congressional Medal awarded, American Battlefield Trust.
* "We the People…", Preamble to the United States Constitution, 1787
* The United States Pledge of Allegiance (4 USC Section 4)

THE BATTLE OF ODELL'S FORD

* Last Will and Testament/Inventory and Appraisement, the Estate of John O'Dell, Laurens County S.C. Probate Court, Bundle (Box) 55, Package 3
* "New Birth of Freedom…", "Gettysburg Address", United States President Abraham Lincoln, 19 November 1863
* "Jordan River, I am…", Writer, Mr Milton Biggham
* "Down by the Riverside", Black Spiritual.
* The United States Pledge of Allegiance (4 USC Section 4)

THE BATTLE OF RIDGEWAY'S FORT

* John Ridgeway's American Revolutionary pension application, South Carolina Department of Archives and History, Columbia, South Carolina.
* The United States Pledge of Allegiance (4 USC Section 4)

THE BATTLE OF HAYES' STATION

* Last Will and Testament/Inventory and Appraisement, the Estate of Joseph Hayes, Abbeville County, S.C. Probate Court, Box 45, Package 1828
* "(Thomas) Sumter's Law", (1781), codified February, 1782, South Carolina legislature
* The United States Pledge of Allegiance (4 USC Section 4)

THE BATTLE OF KELLET'S BLOCKHOUSE

* Statute for South Carolina Historical Marker, H 3259, 117th Session, a Concurrent Resolution
* Last Will and Testament/Inventory and Appraisement, the Estate of Joseph Kellet, Laurens County, S.C. Probate Court. Estate Record Book A-1, Page 4
* "I Have a Dream…" Speech by the Reverend Dr Martin Luther King, Jr, 28 August 1963

* The United States Pledge of Allegiance (4 USC Section 4)

THE BATTLE OF KING'S MOUNTAIN

* Inventory and Appraisement the Estate of James Williams, Laurens County SC Probate Court, Estate Record Book A-1, Page 253
* The Scrap Book (1982). Laurens County Historical Society and Laurens County Arts Council
* The United States Pledge of Allegiance (4 USC Section 4)

YORKTOWN

* Francis Scott Key's "Slaves", US National Park Service
* Mr William Lee, United States President, George Washington's Mount Vernon, Virginia
* George Washington and Slavery, Mount Vernon, Virginia
* Washington's Life Saved, National Association for the Advancement of Coloured People, "The Crisis" (December, 1916).
* "I Have a Dream…" Speech by the Reverend Dr Martin Luther King, Jr, 28 August 1963.
* "Gettysburg Address", United States President Abraham Lincoln, 19 November 1863.

* Reconstruction, United States President, Rutherford B. Hayes, 1887–1881.
* The United States Pledge of Allegiance (4 USC Section 4)